Sensational Story

3D

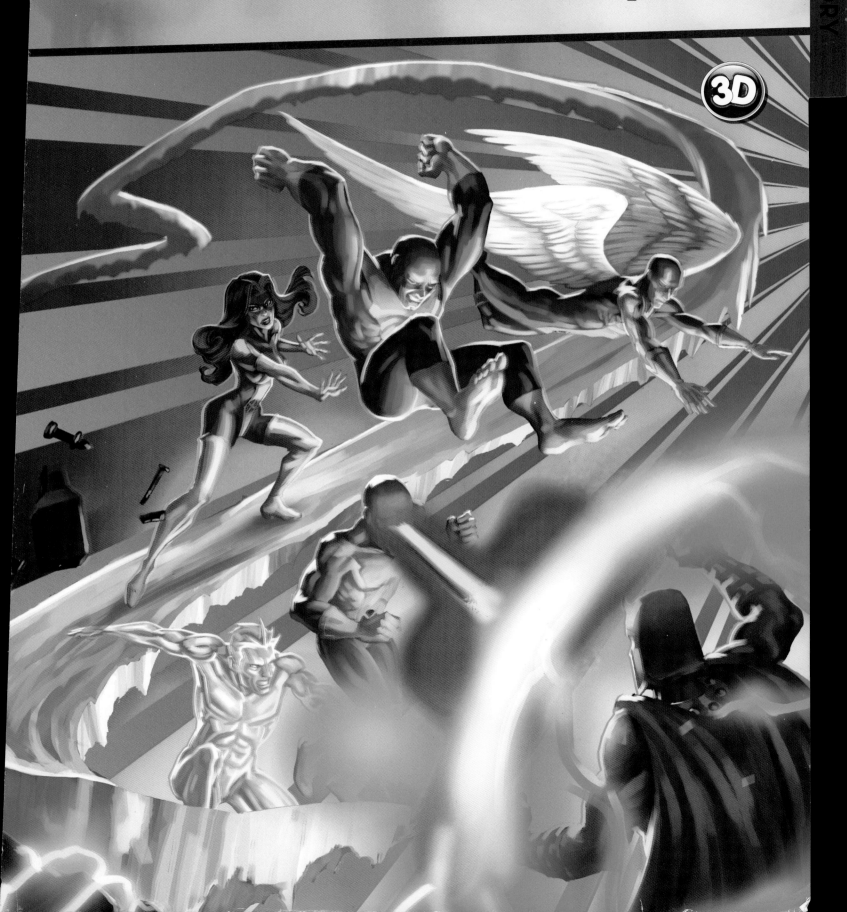

AN ORIGIN STORY

Did you ever have a dream that felt so real, that you were sure you weren't dreaming at all? This is a story about a boy named Charles Xavier who dreamed he could do many things that an ordinary boy could not.

He dreamed his mind could leave his body and float like a feather.

He dreamed he could know what other people were thinking before they even opened their mouths to speak.

But Charles didn't want to tell other people about his special dreams, because he was afraid of how they would treat him. So Charles dreamed of a world where people like himself—people who felt different—could be proud to be themselves.

But those dreams would always end abruptly.

You see, the world didn't seem like a very fair place to Charles.

3D

His father had passed away when he was just a young boy. He lived in his father's mansion with his mother, who loved him very much. But his older brother and his stepfather lived in the mansion, too. And they were heartless and cruel to Charles and his mother.

Charles didn't look like other kids either. He began to lose his hair at a very young age. And by the time he was a teenager, Charles' head was completely bare.

But that was not all.

Charles had always heard whispers of things that no one was saying out loud.

As he grew older, he began to hear them more and more clearly. Eventually Charles realized that **he could read minds.**

As time went by and Charles grew older, he used his gift to gain knowledge. He studied to become a doctor of science. He wanted to learn more about why he had these special powers.

Charles soon discovered that he was a mutant—**a person born with special abilities.**

His studies took him all over the world. And while in Egypt, Charles met another mutant for the first time.

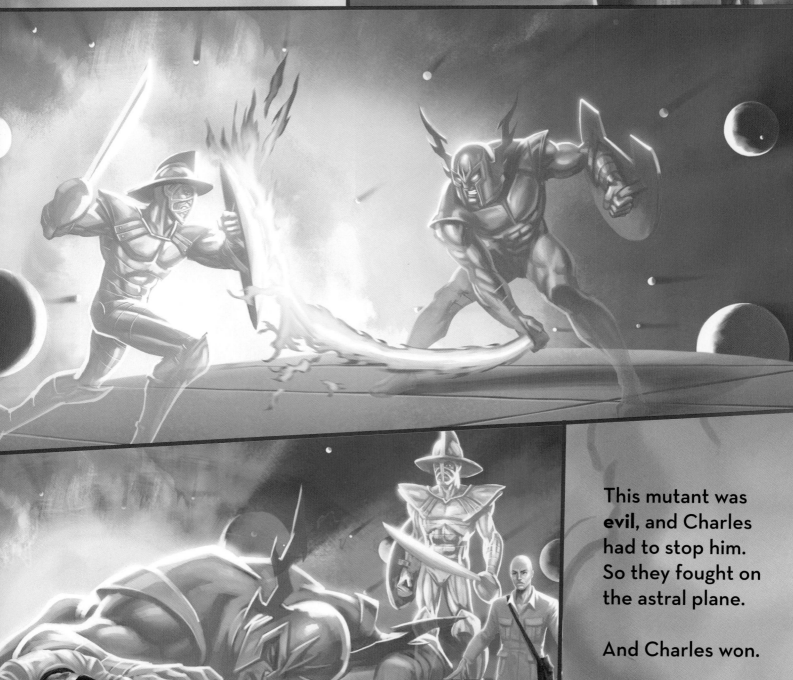

This mutant was **evil**, and Charles had to stop him. So they fought on the astral plane.

And Charles won.

Charles soon met another mutant—a man named **Erik Magnus**. Magnus had the mutant power to move metal objects without touching them. Charles and Magnus became fast friends. But they did not always agree.

Magnus knew humans feared and hated mutants. He thought the only way for mutants to keep themselves safe was to use their powers to take over the world. But Charles still dreamed of a world where humans and mutants could live together **peacefully**.

Charles and Magnus met and defeated an **evil human** named **Baron von Strucker** who wanted to use his wealth to destroy anyone he didn't like.

Magnus felt that this proved humans were bad. He took the baron's gold and flew away with it, telling Charles he was foolish to believe that mankind was good.

Charles was sad to lose his friend. As he continued his travels, he began to think about returning home. But during a stop on his journey, Charles encountered an alien named Lucifer. He wanted to destroy both humans and mutants.

They fought, and the alien brought down his secret hideaway on top of Charles. Charles survived, but his legs had been crushed. **He would never again be able to walk.**

He returned home, more determined than ever to find other mutants. He would train them to fight any threat—mutant, human, or alien.

Charles' mother and stepfather had passed away, and his brother had left the mansion long ago. The Xavier home was empty, but it **wouldn't stay that way for long.**

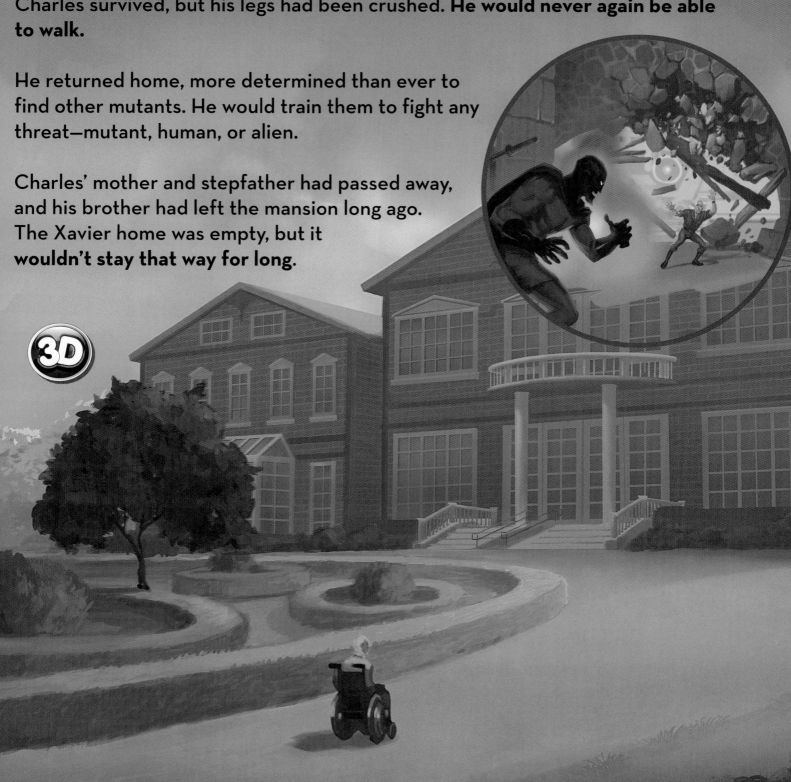

The first mutant Charles found was named **Scott Summers.** Charles called him **Cyclops** for the optic blasts he could shoot from his eyes.

Next, Charles and Cyclops rescued a teenager from an angry mutant-hating mob.

The boy, **Bobby Drake,** could turn himself into ice and called himself **Iceman.**

Then the growing group found **Warren Warthington III,** who called himself **Angel** for the wings that helped him fly.

And finally **Hank McCoy** joined the team. Hank was called **The Beast** because of his large hands and feet, which helped him swing like a monkey and punch like a gorilla.

Charles renamed the mansion **Xavier's School for Gifted Youngsters**.
To the outside world, it was just another boarding school. But secretly, it was a school for young mutants to learn how to use their powers. The students were given uniforms, and each pledged to fight for Charles' dream.

Charles called himself **Professor X** and his team the **X-Men**, because each member had an extraordinary power.

The X-Men soon welcomed their fifth and final founding member—**Jean Grey**, called **Marvel Girl**. Jean could move things with her mind.

Professor X then built a computer to locate other mutants. The machine, called **Cerebro**, showed that a mutant was attacking an army base.

It was the Professor's old friend Magnus!

Now known as **Magneto**, he had used the baron's gold to wage war on the human race. Charles knew that only the **X-Men** could stop his old friend!

The X-Men arrived at the base just as Magneto began to attack.
And so the X-Men sprang into action and attacked him right back.

Cyclops tried to **blast** through Magneto's magnetic field. But he couldn't.

Magneto guided every **missile** that Marvel Girl tried to send at him right back at her.

Angel and The Beast did not fare much better.

At last, Magneto attacked them all. But Marvel Girl covered her teammates with a **force field**.

The X-Men were not so easily defeated!

The X-Men had come to stop Magneto and turn him over to the police. **But Magneto had escaped.**

Over the next few months, the X-Men trained in a special gym called the **Danger Room.** The room was filled with obstacles to help the X-Men perfect their abilities. And Professor X used Cerebro to keep a constant watch for **new mutants.**

And he found many! But more often than not, the mutants were evil.

After many battles, the X-Men graduated and became full-fledged heroes. Professor X had never been prouder of his students.

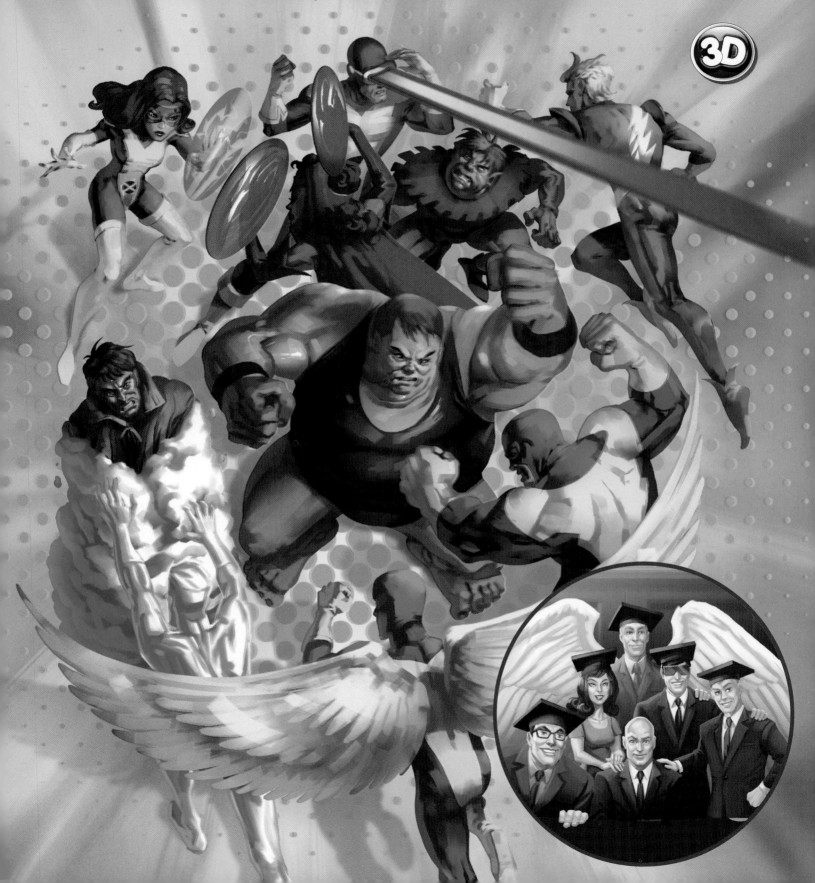

He retired their school uniforms and dressed them in new costumes. But the end of their school days did not mean the end of their missions. In fact, things only got more difficult for the X-Men.

More mutants were appearing each day, and humans were becoming more and more concerned. They were afraid of the mutants' powers. Even though the X-Men tried to protect humans and live Professor Xavier's dream, people treated **all** mutants badly.

As mutants grew in number, so did the **X-Men**. Cyclops' brother **Alex Summers**—an energy-blasting mutant called **Havok**—and **Lorna Dane**, called **Polaris** for her magnetic abilities, joined the team.

Toronto

Dublin

Moscow

Berlin

But their group was still too small to fight all of the threats. And when the X-Men went missing on a dangerous mission, Professor X had to assemble a **new group** to rescue them.

Nairobi

In Canada, he recruited a mutant named Wolverine who could heal himself of any injury and whose claws could cut through almost anything!

In Germany, Charles found **Kurt Wagner**, called **Nightcrawler**, who could move from place to place with just a thought. Together with Wolverine and Nightcrawler, Professor X decided to seek out more good mutants to help rescue the original X-Men.

3D

In Ireland, Charles found **Sean Cassidy**—**Banshee**—whose sonic scream could shatter stone and steel.

In Africa, Charles met **Ororo Munroe**, a weather mutant called **Storm**.

And in Russia, the mutant **Peter Rasputin**—called **Colossus** because he could turn himself to metal— bid a tearful farewell to his family to join the professor.

Charles' new international team wasted no time in their search to find **the original X-Men**.

The new X-Men rescued the original team from **Krakoa, the living island!**

3D

The new group decided to stay at Xavier's school. They trained to use
their powers. Soon they too became X-Men. They were a kind of family.
But no matter what the X-Men did trouble seemed to find them.
No matter the day, month, or season...

...the X-Men were never safe.

Enemies both old and new were always attacking. And with every incident, humans became more worried about mutants.

But with every battle, Charles felt the need to fight harder for his dream. And whenever Charles felt hope leaving him, he'd lie down, just as he did when he was a boy, close his eyes, drift off to sleep...and dream.

Incredible Activities

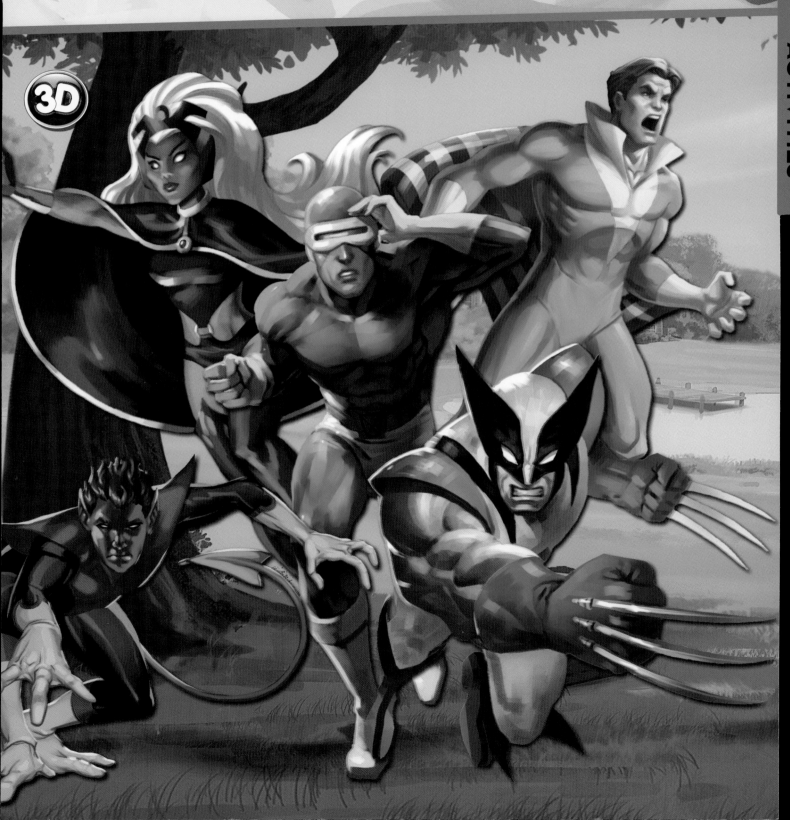

3D

Use your most powerful pens and pencils to complete the incredible activities.

The X-Men are training in the Danger Room. Color in the mighty mutants!

Connect each X-Man to the picture that best matches his or her powers.

**Can you find the names of the following
X-Men in the puzzle below? Look up, down,
backward, forward, and diagonally.**

ANGEL BANSHEE BEAST COLOSSUS CYCLOPS HAVOK

ICEMAN POLARIS PROFESSOR X STORM WOLVERINE

```
H S P O L A R I S B
C A L P W I C C L A
Y X V W O L V E O N
C S T O R M G M R S
L P V L K N G A M X
O A T S A E B N G E
P R O F E S S O R X
S E E H S N A B C R
C O L O S S U S V M
W E N I R E V L O W
```

Answers:
```
W O L V E R I N E W
M V S U S S O L O C
R C B A N S H E E S
X R O S S E F O R P
E G N B E A S T A O
X M A G N K L V P L
S R M G M R O T S C
N O E V L O W V X Y
A L C C I W P L A C
B S I R A L O P S H
```

Which staircase should Wolverine take to the Control Room?

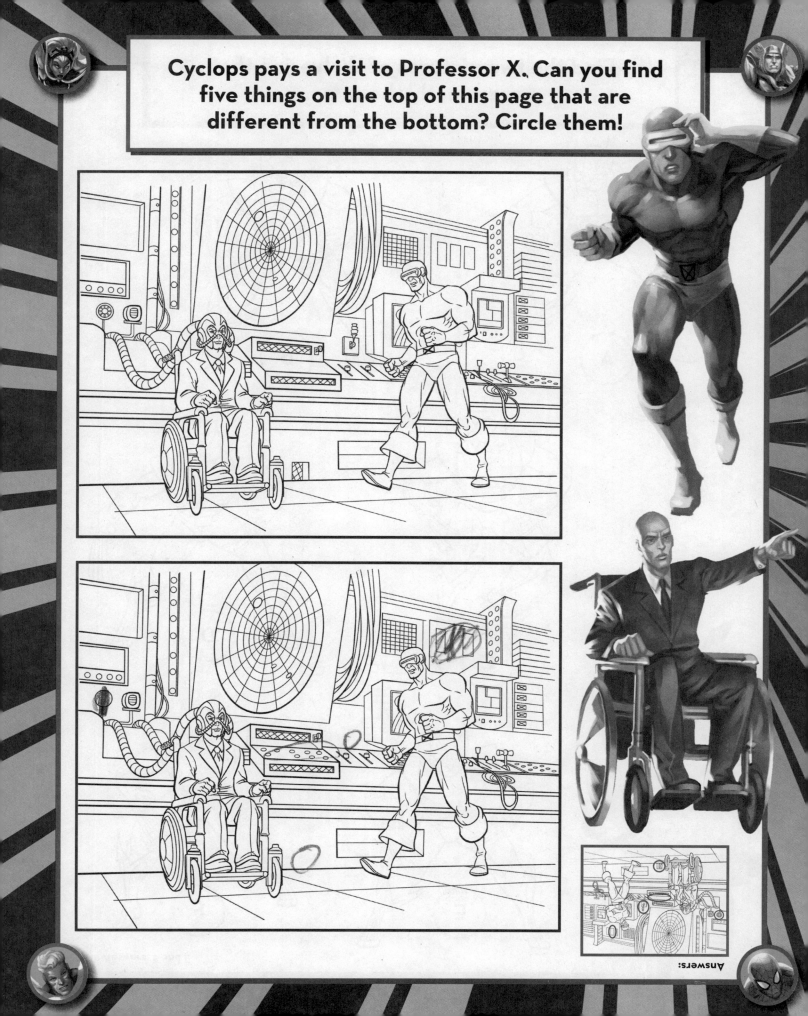

Cyclops pays a visit to Professor X. Can you find five things on the top of this page that are different from the bottom? Circle them!

Find the two pictures of Wolverine that are exactly the same.

A

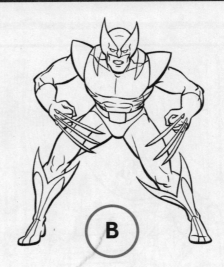

B

C

D

E

F

Connect the dots to see where Tony Stark stores his Iron Man costume.

How many words can you spell using the letters in STARK INDUSTRIES?

RUST

_____   _____

_____   _____

_____   _____

_____   _____

_____   _____

_____   _____

_____   _____

Friend or foe? Circle the three Iron Man enemies.

Pepper Potts

Happy Hogan

The Mandarin

Ezekiel Stane

James Rhodes

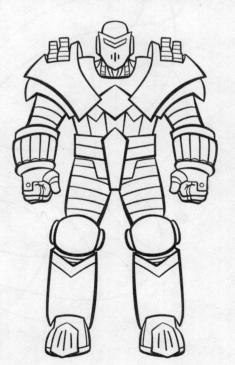

Crimson Dynamo

Help Iron Man follow the correct signal back to the Controller's hideout.

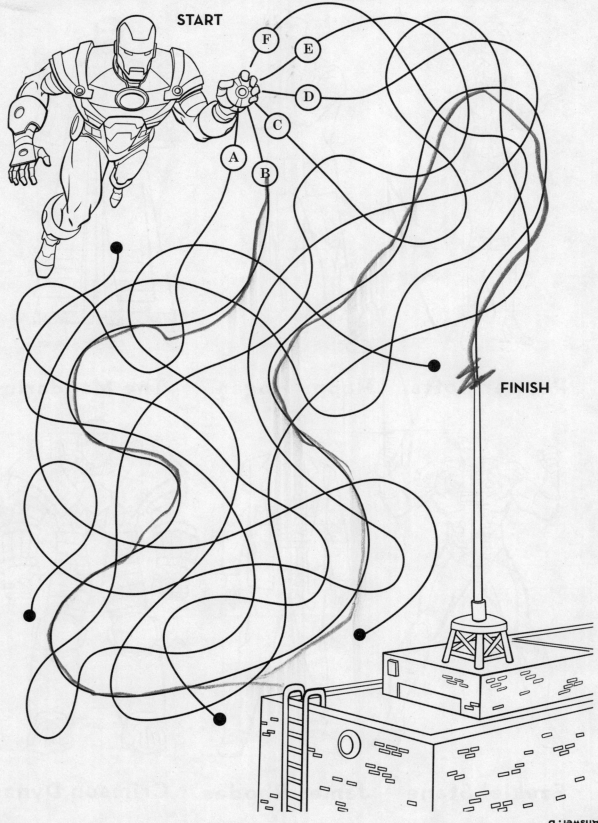

START

F
E
D
C
A
B

FINISH

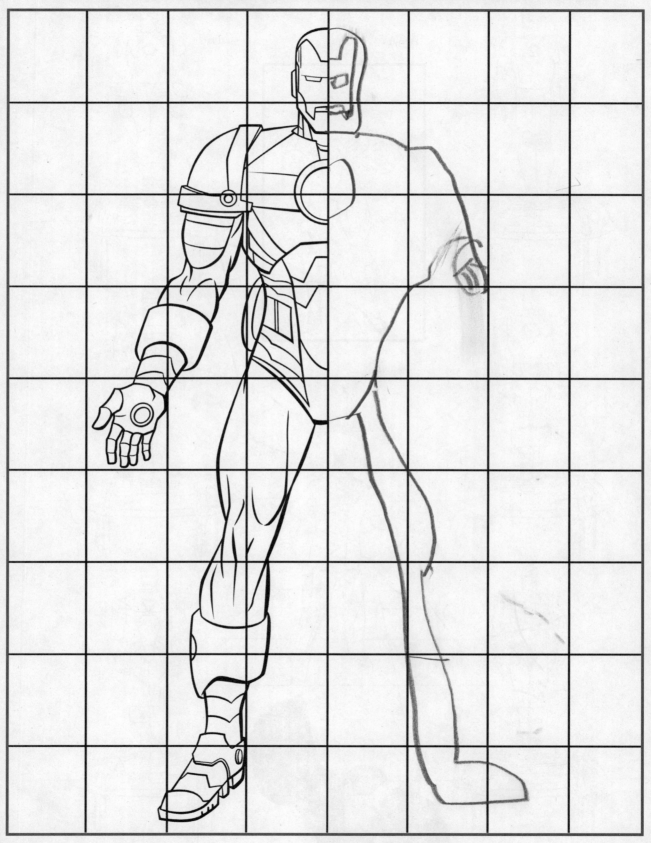

Help Tony Stark pick the correct suit of armor.

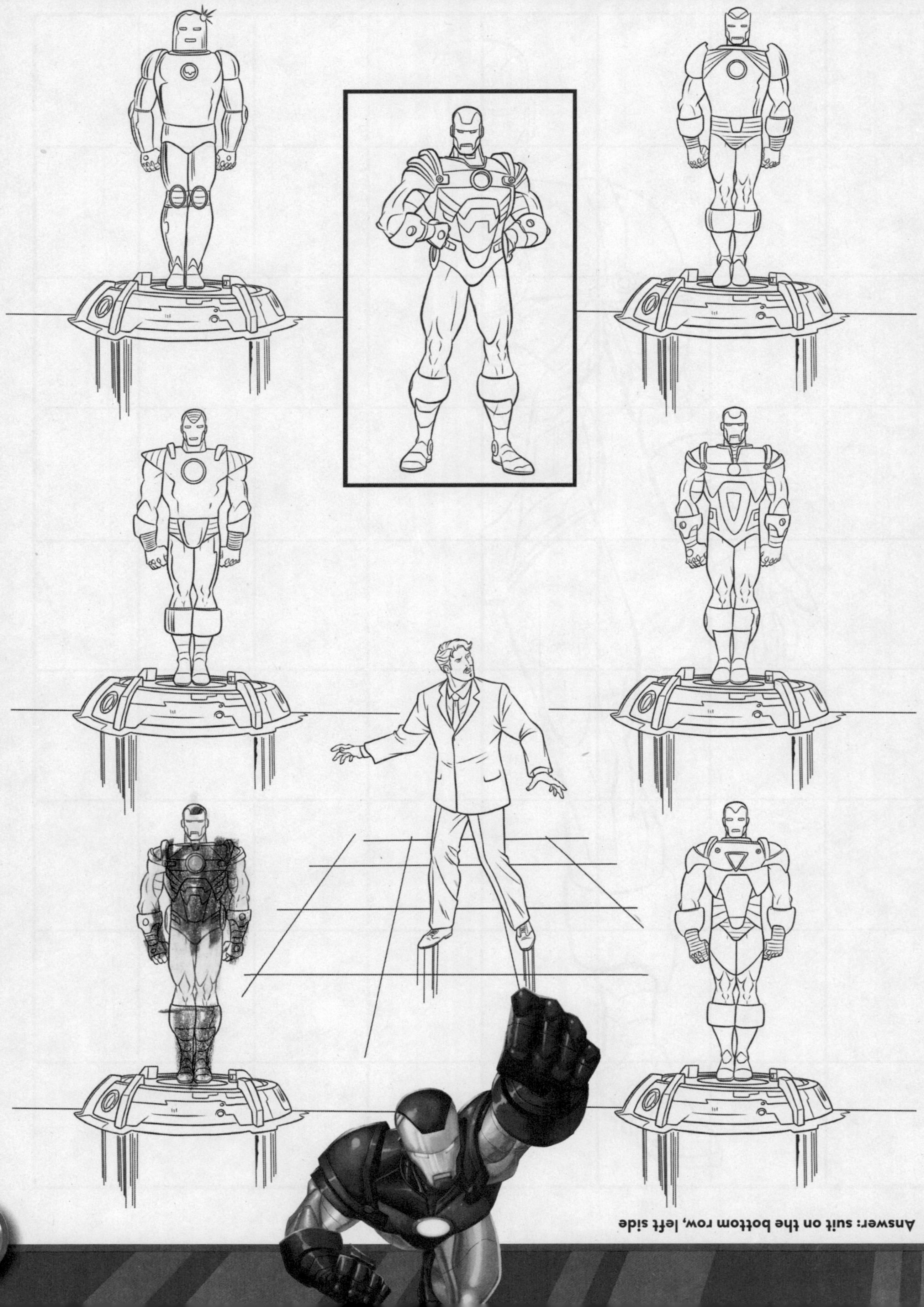

Answer: suit on the bottom row, left side

Help Iron Man give his armor the proper command. Replace each letter with the letter that comes before it in the alphabet.

TFDVSF BJSUJHIU TFBM

_ _ _ _ _ _   _ _ _ _ _ _ _ _

_ _ _ _

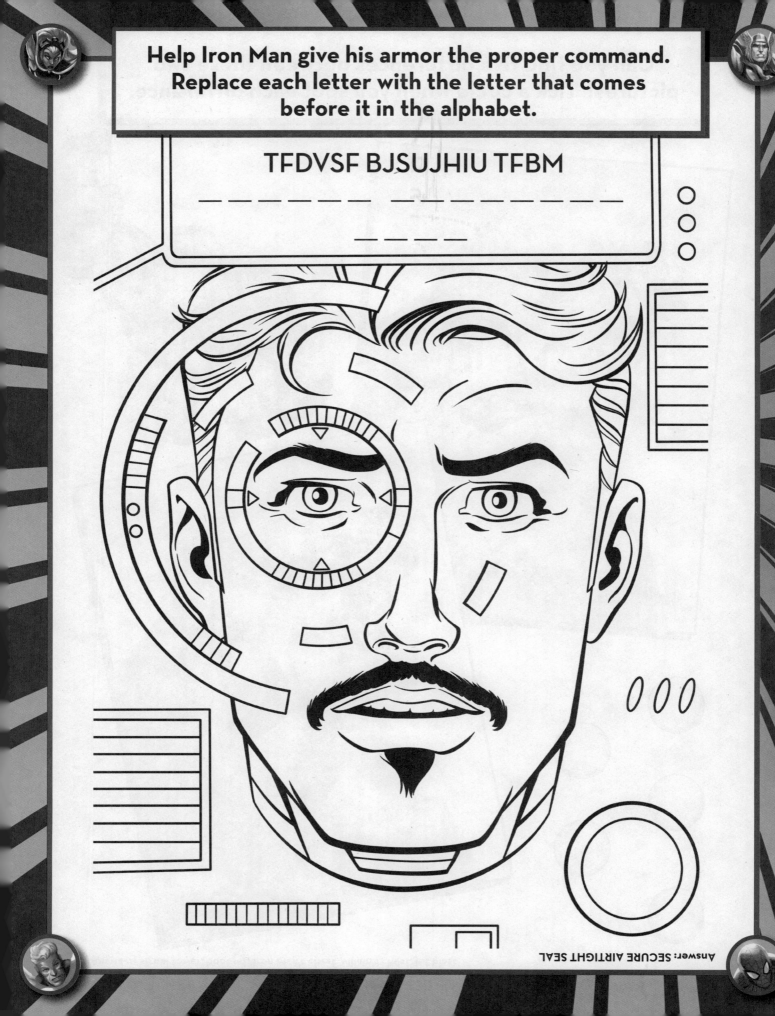

Can you find five differences between these two pictures? Tick a circle when you spot each difference.

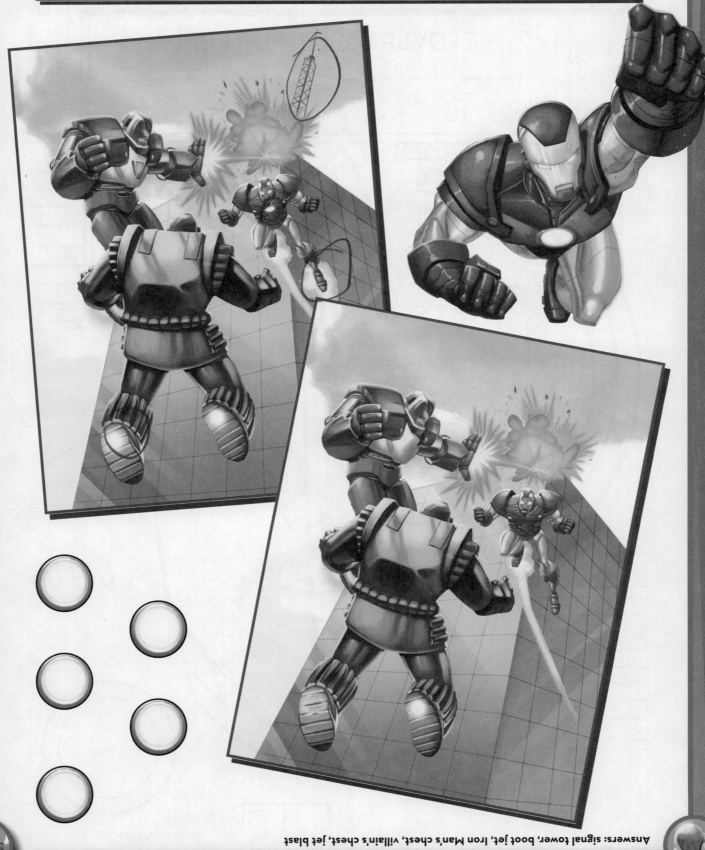

Help Thor and Balder find the correct path to Asgard!

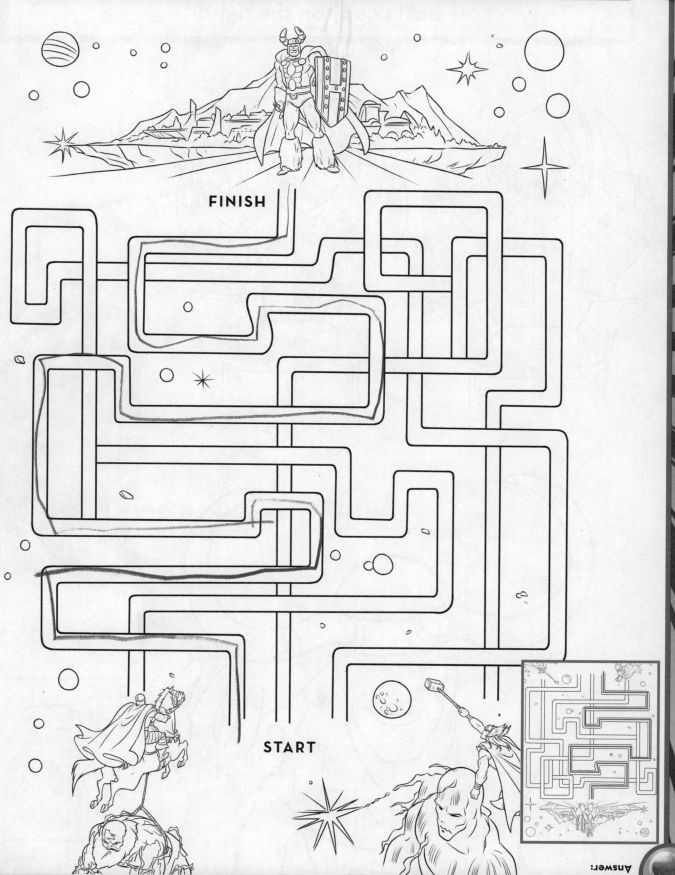

FINISH

START

Loki has made a copy of Odin's throne. Spot five differences between the real throne on the left and Loki's copy on the right!

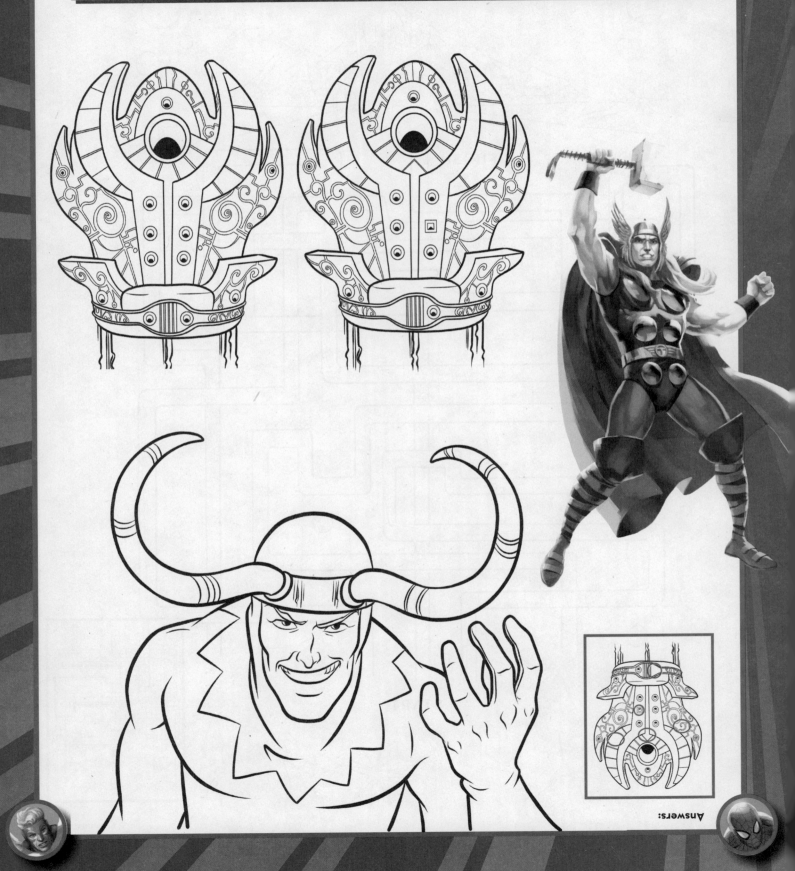

Answers:

The Storm Giant is causing destruction. Find ten differences between the picture of the block before the Storm Giant arrived and the picture of the block after!

BEFORE

AFTER

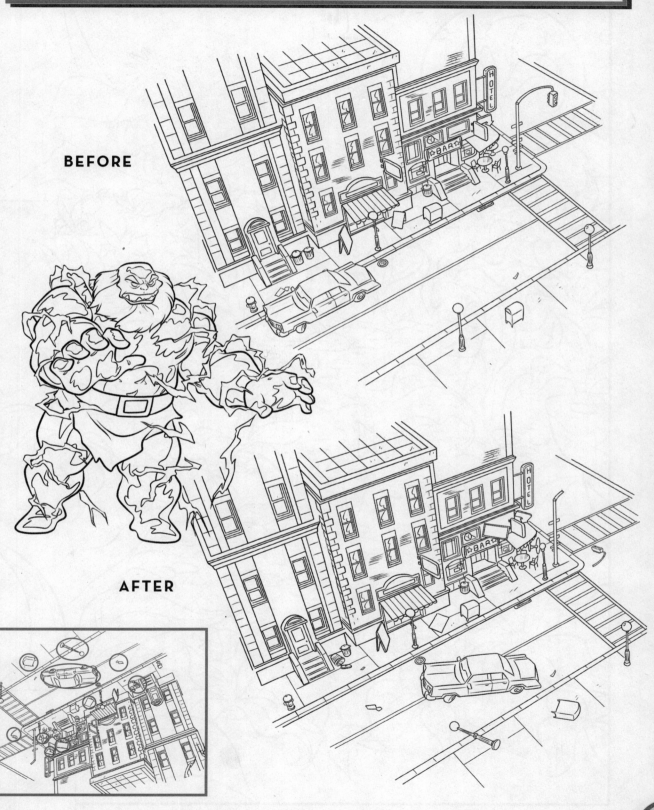

Volstagg's helmet will show Thor where his friends are. Help Thor find it!

Thor has created a whirlwind to send Loki and the gremlins back to Asgard. Draw it, making sure it covers Loki and the gremlins!

Friend or foe? Loki has transformed five trolls into copies of Captain America. Help Thor find the real Cap!

Help Captain America decode the message!

☐ = A   ■ = E   0 = I   ▮ = M   ⋅⋅ = O   ∘∘ = T

▤ = C   ▢ = G   ☰ = K   ⋅⋅ = N   ⦂ = S   ◐ = Z

ZEMO IS

ATTACKING

Spot the fake! Five of these pictures show the real Hulk. One is a troll in disguise!

Help Hulk hold up the damaged bridge by connecting the dots!

Gamma smash! Which two pictures of Hulk are exactly the same?

Bruce Banner lost six important things the last time he transformed. Help him find them!

Help Spidey snag Electro with his web-shooter.
Circle the correct web-shot!

Which photo of Spider-Man is exactly the same as the main picture?

Five members of the police arrive at a scene. Help Spider-Man find the police in the crowd!

Show the heroes the way through Asgard to the waiting ship!

Search up, down, forward, backward, and diagonally to find all the names of the heroes.

```
K L U H M C Y
I J Q L I B R
K R V R A R U
P L O C N Y P
S H J N T S A
T X A W M D C
H S R C A A O
V P V P N F N
C J I O G R E
W A S P O T E
```

Help the heroes find the attack site!

START

FINISH

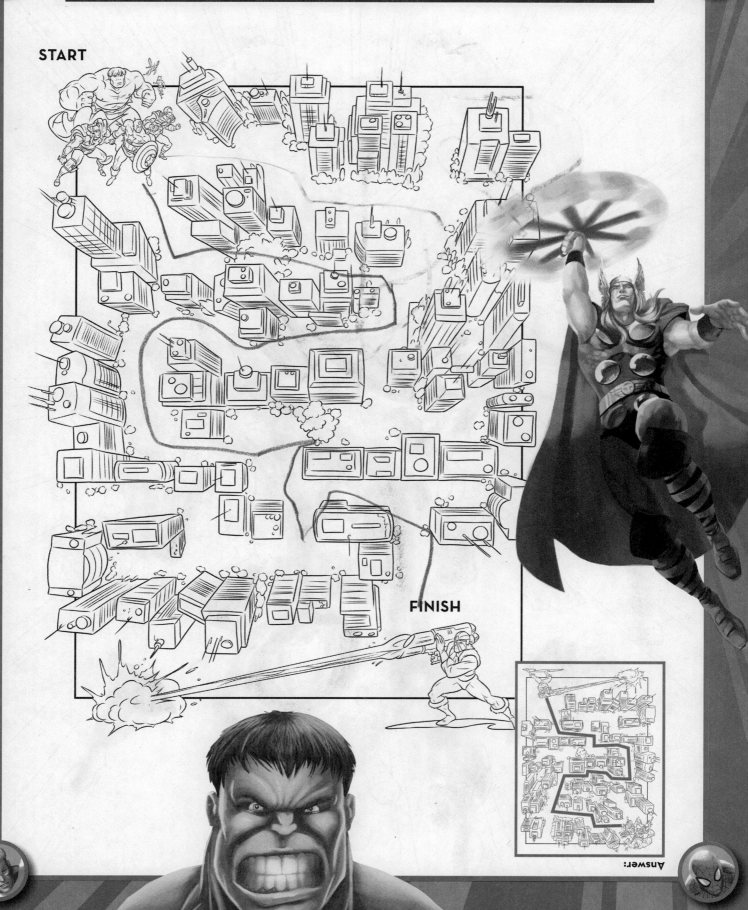

Color in this incredible action picture!

Press-Out and Play

Press out and play with every card page. There's a Marvel hanging mobile, hero masks, super stencils, amazing bookmarks and a cool door hanger!

Marvel Mobile

How to make:
1. Ask an adult to help you cut five different lengths of different colored ribbon.
2. Press out the hero shapes. Thread a piece of ribbon through each loop and knot or fix with sticky tape. Tape the other end of each ribbon to the back of the square shape.
3. When all the shapes are attached, press out the circle in the middle of the square, thread the last piece of ribbon through it and knot firmly. Hang it wherever you like!

Amazing Bookmarks

Press out the bookmarks to keep track of the best bits in your favorite books.

3D

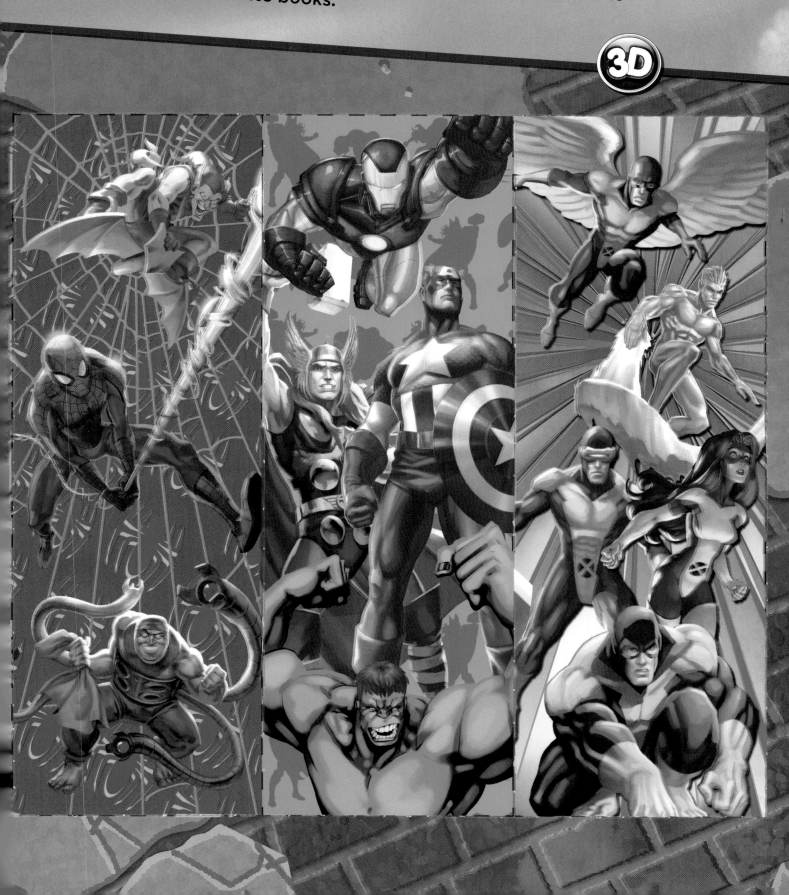

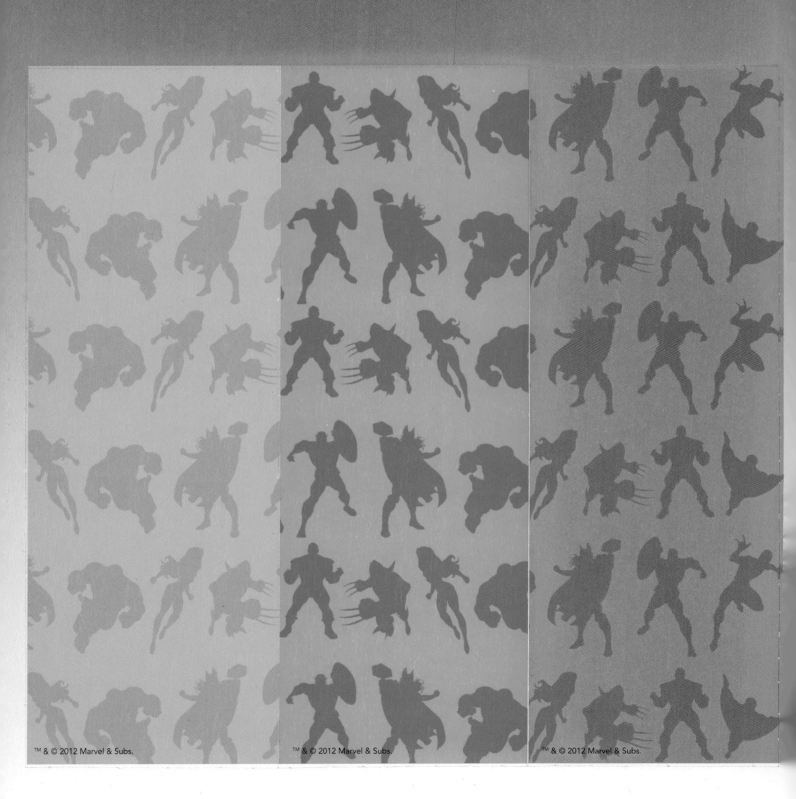

Make Your Own
Amazing Adventure

3D

ADVENTURE

Use your stencils, stickers and favorite pencils to draw a heroic story about the mightiest heroes in the world.
Who will the heroes battle in your story?

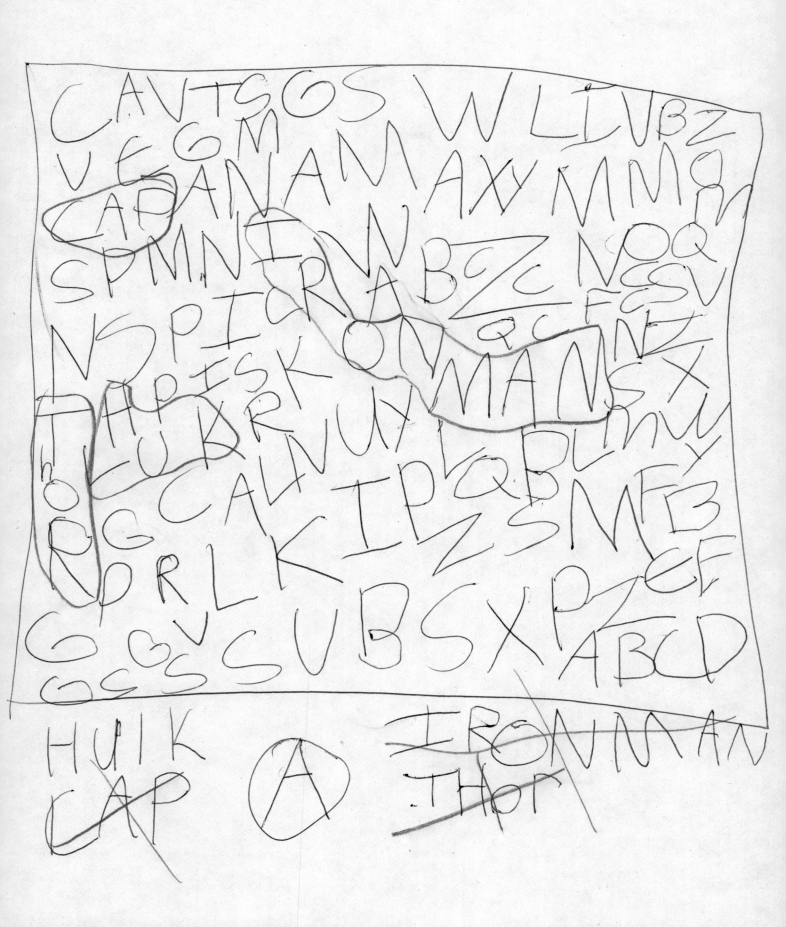

My Super Hero Scrapbook

3D

THOR

CAPTAIN AMERICA

WOLVERINE

The Marvel Super Heroes live for adventure, discovery and daring deeds. Remember all your explorations and adventures in this scrapbook.